S/JGN

Will   Irma   Taranee   Cornelia   Hay Lin

GRAPHIC NOVEL #2
MERIDIAN MAGIC

W.i.t.c.h.

Will   Irma   Taranee   Cornelia   Hay Lin

GRAPHIC NOVEL #2
MERIDIAN MAGIC

an imprint of
HYPERION BOOKS FOR CHILDREN
New York

© 2005 Disney Enterprises, Inc.
W.I.T.C.H., Will Irma Taranee Cornelia Hay Lin is a trademark of Disney Enterprises, Inc.
Volo® is a registered trademark of Disney Enterprises, Inc.
Volo/Hyperion Books for Children are imprints of Disney Children's Book Group, L.L.C.

Printed in the United States of America

First Edition
3 5 7 9 10 8 6 4 2

ISBN 0-7868-0974-4

Visit www.clubwitch.com

... WITH-OUT ANY LIES ...

IS HAY LIN COMING HOME FOR LUNCH?

... A FAMILY LIKE ALL THE OTHERS, WITHOUT ANY SECRETS ...

... WITHOUT ANY MYSTERIES ...

NO ... SHE CALLED FIVE MINUTES AGO. SHE'S AT THE LIBRARY WITH IRMA.

SHE ALWAYS CALLS AT THE LAST MINUTE! SHE HAS TO LEARN THIS IS NOT A RESTAURANT!

BUT DEAR, THIS IS A RESTAURANT!

YOU KNOW WHAT I MEAN! I'M GOING TO TELL HER WHAT I THINK WHEN SHE COMES HOME TONIGHT!

GRUMBLE, GRUMBLE!

WHAT WAS THAT SOUND?

IT WAS MY STOMACH, IRMA. I'M STARVING. IT'S LATE. CAN WE PLEASE GO HOME?

FIRST, I WANT TO FIND OUT MRS. RUDOLPH'S SECRETS.

WHAT SECRETS? SHE SPENT THE WHOLE AFTERNOON GRADING OUR MATH TESTS! WHY CAN'T YOU ADMIT YOU WERE WRONG?

MAYBE I WILL, BUT FIRST I WANT TO CHECK, ONE MORE TIME. I JUST GOT AN IDEA! ARE YOU FREE TOMORROW MORNING?

WE ARE SUPPOSED TO BE IN SCHOOL TOMORROW MORNING.

WHATEVER! WE'LL SPEND ALMOST TWENTY YEARS OF OUR LIFE IN SCHOOL! WE CAN TAKE ONE DAY OFF!

YOU ARE GOING TO RUIN ME. WHEN I FLUNK I'LL KNOW WHO I HAVE TO THANK!

BUT WHAT IF THAT WOMAN REALLY IS A MONSTER? DON'T BE SELFISH, HAY LIN! YOU HAVE A CHANCE TO SAVE THE WORLD!

NO! NO! NO! I DON'T WANT TO. . . .

PLEASE CHANGE YOUR MIND.

OH, FOR HEAVEN'S SAKE! YOU KNOW WHAT?

"OKAY!"

ALL CLEAR?

NOBODY AROUND . . .

21

THE LIGHT OF CANDRACAR AND THE DARKNESS OF METAMOOR CONFRONT EACH OTHER WITHOUT A SOUND. . . .

. . . AND ONCE AGAIN THE HEART PREVAILS.

CREEEAK

I BET YOU WERE TALKING ABOUT BOYS!

UH . . .

GROAN . . .

45

EXCUSE DID YOU USE TO SNEAK
O MRS. RUDOLPH'S?

I SAID WE WERE EATING AT YOUR PARENTS' RESTAURANT! SO, GO WITH THAT, OKAY?

THE PROBLEM IS THAT NOW I'M HUNGRY! I'LL HAVE TO SECRETLY RAID MY FRIDGE BEFORE I GO.

SEE YOU LATER, YOU-KNOW-WHERE! AND WEAR SOMETHING PRACTICAL!

SURE THING!

I HOPE NO ONE IS AROUND. I DON'T WANT TO HAVE TO ANSWER ANY QUESTIONS, LIKE . . .

73

WHERE HAVE YOU BEEN, YOUNG LADY?

I CALLED HAY LIN'S AND THEY TOLD ME YOU WEREN'T THERE!

WE GOT TAKEOUT, MOM. AND ATE IT AT WILL'S.